						2 **He** Helium 4.0
5 **B** Boron 10.8	6 **C** Carbon 12.0	7 **N** Nitrogen 14.0	8 **O** Oxygen 16	9 **F** Fluorine 19.0	10 **Ne** Neon 20.2	
13 **Al** Aluminum 27.0	14 **Si** Silicon 28.1	15 **P** Phosphorus 31	16 **S** Sulfur 32.1	17 **Cl** Chlorine 35.5	18 **Ar** Argon 40.0	

28 **Ni** Eckel 58.7	29 **Cu** Copper 63.5	30 **Zn** Zinc 65.4	31 **Ga** Gallium 69.7	32 **Ge** Germanium 72.6	33 **As** Arsenic 74.9	34 **Se** Selenium 79.0	35 **Br** Bromine 79.9	36 **Kr** Krypton 83.8
46 **Pd** adium 06.4	47 **Ag** Silver 107.9	48 **Cd** Cadmium 112.4	49 **In** Indium 114.8	50 **Sn** Tin 118.7	51 **Sb** Antimony 121.8	52 **Te** Tellurium 127.6	53 **I** Iodine 126.9	54 **Xe** Xenon 131.3
78 **Pt** tinum 95.1	79 **Au** Gold 197.0	80 **Hg** Mercury 200.6	81 **Tl** Thallium 204.4	82 **Pb** Lead 207.2	83 **Bi** Bismuth 209.0	84 **Po** Polonium 210.0	85 **At** Astatine 210.0	86 **Rn** Radon 222.0
.10 **Ds** stadtium 271	111 **Uuu** Unununium 272	112 **Uub** Ununbium 277		114 **Uuq** Ununquadium 296		116 **Uuh** Ununhexium 298		

SCIENCE VERSE

JON SCIESZKA AND LANE SMITH

SCHOLASTIC INC.

New York   Toronto   London   Auckland   Sydney
Mexico City   New Delhi   Hong Kong   Buenos Aires

ISBN 0-439-79329-7

Text copyright © 2004 by Jon Scieszka. Illustrations copyright © 2004 by Lane Smith.
All rights reserved. Published by Scholastic Inc., 557 Broadway, New York, NY 10012,
by arrangement with Viking Children's Books, a member of Penguin Group (USA) Inc.
SCHOLASTIC and associated logos are trademarks and/or registered trademarks
of Scholastic Inc.

12 11 10 9 8 7 6 5 4 3 2   5 6 7 8 9 10/0

Printed in Singapore   46

First Scholastic printing, September 2005

Set in Franklin Gothic

DESIGN: MOLLY LEACH

TO? FOR? Six, eight.
Who do we appreciate?

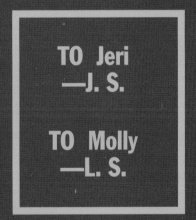

TO Jeri
—J. S.

TO Molly
—L. S.

ON WEDNESDAY in science class, Mr. Newton says,

"You know, if you listen closely enough, you can hear the poetry of science in everything."

I listen closely. On Thursday, I start hearing the poetry. In fact, I start hearing everything as a science poem.

Mr. Newton has zapped me with a curse of SCIENCE VERSE.

EVOLUTION

Glory, glory, evolution.
Darwin found us a solution.
Your mama is that shape,
And your knuckles always scrape . . .
'Cause Grandpa was an ape.

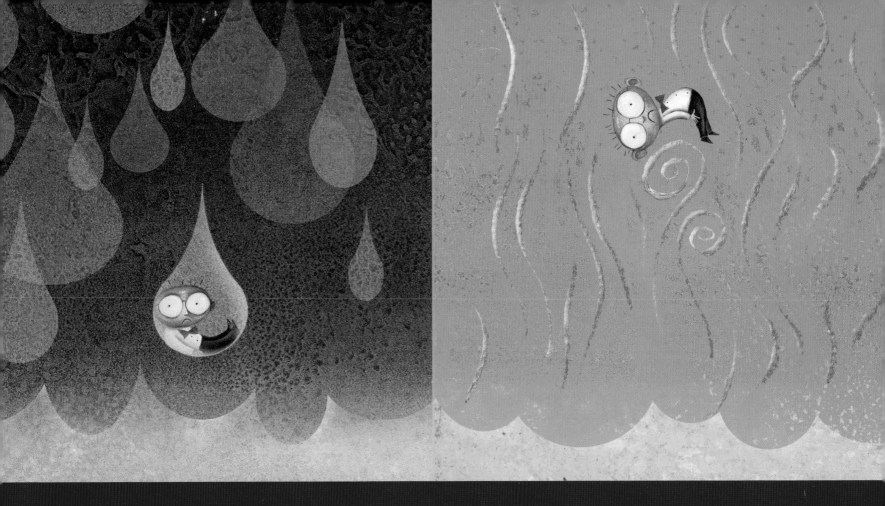

WATER CYCLE

It's raining, it's pouring.
For H_2O, it's boring:
Precipitation,
Evaporation,
Precipitation,
Evaporation,
Precipitation,
Evaporation . . .
Evening, night, and morning.

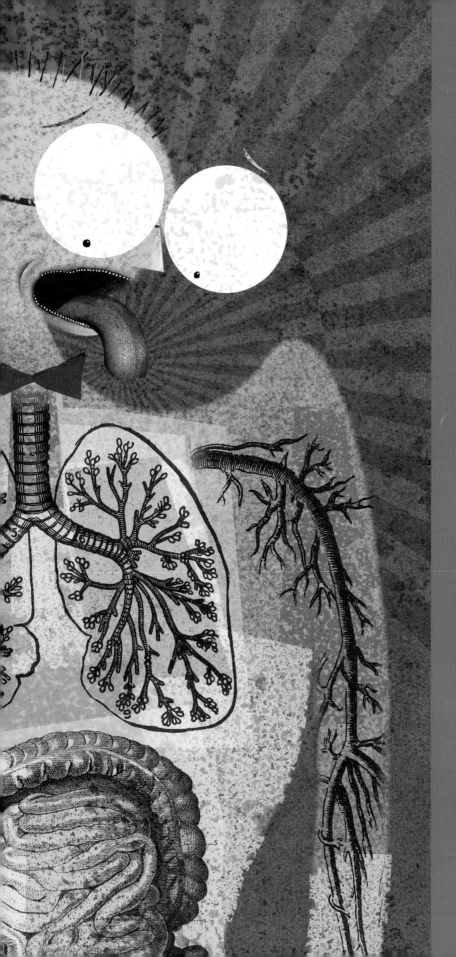

LOVELY

I think that I ain't never seen
A poem ugly as a spleen.

A poem that could make you shiver,
Like 3.5 . . . pounds of liver.

A poem to make you lose your lunch,
Tie your intestines in a bunch.

A poem all gray, wet, and swollen,
Like a stomach or a colon.

Something like your kidney, lung,
Pancreas, bladder, even tongue.

Why you turning green, good buddy?
It's just human body study.

TWINK—

Twinkle-less, twinkle-less
Spot of black,
In the starry
Zodiac.

Sucking in all
Matter and light.
Turning sunshine
Into night.

Twinkle-less, twinkle-less—
LOST CONTROL!
Now we're trapped in
the black hole.

DINO-SORE

Once in first grade I was napping
When I heard a scary yapping,
Frightful word—worse than a slapping,
Worse than twenty T. rex roars.

Said our teacher, heartless creature,
"My class, you know, always explores
Ten full weeks of . . . DINOSAURS."

Pterodactyl, Stegosaurus,
On and on the same old chorus,
Elementary stuff to bore us.
"No more," we beg. She ignores.

"Yes." She smiles. "They were reptiles."
Then locks the windows, bolts the doors.
"Don't you just love . . . DINOSAURS?"

Every year the scene repeated.
Third grade, fourth grade, we were greeted
With that torture just completed.
Yes, we've heard of carnivores.

Still the teachers changed no features,
Still spoke those words that gave brain sores:
"This year's topic . . . DINOSAURS."

It's still a mystery, scientists say,
Why the dinosaur went away.
But I know why they couldn't stay
(And it wasn't meteors).

It was creatures—yes, those teachers—
Who did the work of fifty wars
And bored to death . . . DINOSAURS.

FOOD CHAIN

Can't you see the green plants growing?
That's energy, okay?
Consumer eats up the producer,
Predator eats prey.

I've been working in the food chain,
All the livelong day.
In the middle of the food chain,
I've got no time to play.

Who's for lunch today?
Who's for lunch today?
Don't you just wonder, who's for lunch today?
Predator or prey.
Predator or prey.
Eat or be eaten, that's the only way.

GOBBLEGOOKY

'Twas fructose, and the vitamins
Did zinc and dye (red #8).
All poly were the thiamins,
And the carbohydrate.

Beware the Gobblegook, my son!
The flavorings, the added C!
Beware the serving size, and shun
The dreaded BHT.

And as in folic thought I stood,
The Gobblegook, with eyes nitrate,
Came gluten through the dextrose wood,
Its extracts carbonate.

Oh, can you slay the Gobblegook,
Polyunsaturated boy?
3,000 calories! Don't look!
The sugars! Fats! Oh soy.

'Twas fructose, and the vitamins
Did zinc and dye (red #8).
All poly were the thiamins,
And the carbohydrate.

WHY SCIENTISTS DON'T WRITE NURSERY RHYMES

Hey Diddle Diddle

Hey diddle diddle, what kind of riddle
Is this nature of light?
Sometimes it's a wave,
Other times particle . . .
But which answer will be marked right?

Mary Had a . . .

Mary had a little worm.
She thought it was a chigger.
But everything that Mary ate,
Only made it bigger.

It came with her to school one day,
And gave the kids a fright,
Especially when the teacher said,
"Now that's a parasite."

Jack Be Nimble

Jack be nimble, Jack be quick.
Jack jump over the combustion reaction of O_2 + heat + fuel to form CO_2 + light + heat + exhaust.

Good Night

Good night, sleep tight,
Don't let the bedbug,
  tick, or louse
  suck blood from you,
  hatch its eggs,
  and then develop the larvae on you
  . . . all right?

SCIENTIFIC METHOD AT THE BAT

The outlook wasn't brilliant for my experiment that day;
The only way to graduate was to come up with an A.
So when my lab exploded and turned to blackish gunk,
My chance of passing anything went Titanic—you know, sunk.

I sat and sadly watched the clock, cursed to be alive.
It would take a miracle—no, make that two—to get me to grade five.
Then I had a brainstorm, an idea so terrific:
I just had to use those words from the METHOD SCIENTIFIC.

I grab my pen and get to work. You should see my look.
I slowly write Hypothesis . . . Observation . . . in my book.
And now the class bell rings. And now I lose or win.
With one mighty PLOP, I hand my lab book in.

Oh somewhere in some science class, hypotheses are made.
Experiments are conducted. Kids move up a grade.
Somewhere conclusions are concluded, without a bit of doubt.
But there is no joy in this lab—my results got me flunked out.

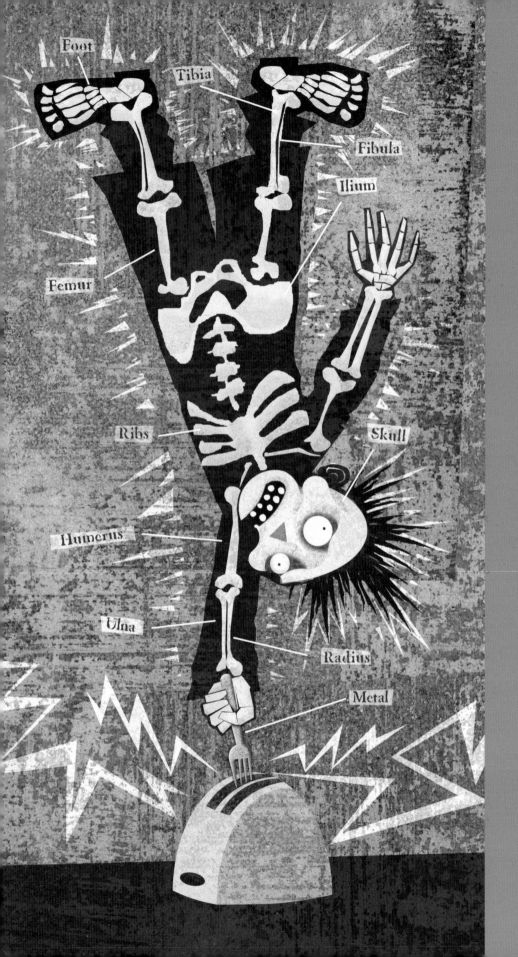

SKELETAL STUDY

There once was a man of science,
Not one of your mental giants.
He decided to settle
The question: Does metal
Fix an electric appliance?

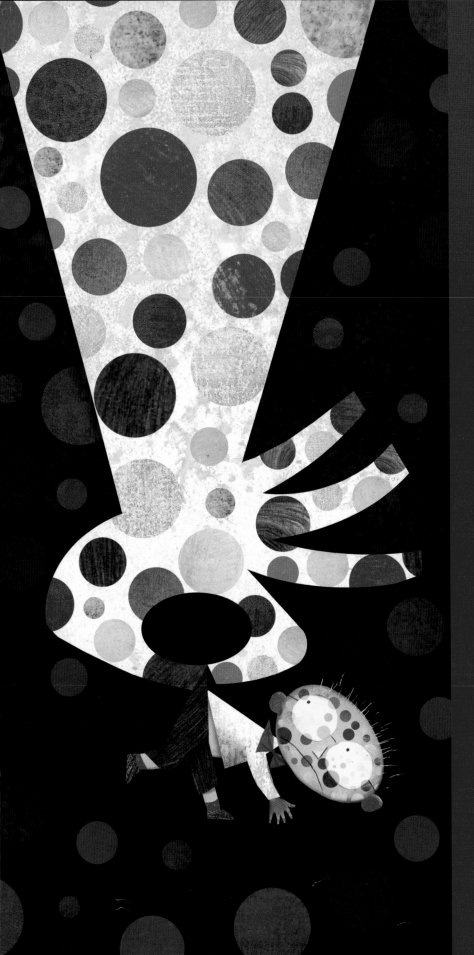

YOU'RE IT

Eenie, meanie, mynie, mo.
Catch a virus, watch it grow.
Once it's got you, it won't go.
Eeenie, meanie, my—oh no!

MINI HA HA (OR, THE ATOMIC JOKE IS ON YOU)

From the shining Big-Sea-Water
To the trees near Gitche Gumee,
Every thing is made of atoms,
Tiny things that you can not see.
Though I have just one small question.
(And I don't ask just to blame them.)
Scientists can't see these things, so
How the heck then can they name them?

NUCLEUS, they call the center,
Made of parts that they call PROTONS,
And more itty-bitty pieces—
Go ahead and call them NEUTRONS.
FLAVORED QUARKS, ELECTRONS, BOSONS—
Things could hardly get more doofy.
I say we think up our own names,
But let's make them way more goofy.

Let us call the proton WA'WA,[1]
The electron, MAHNOMO'NEE.[2]
Call the neutron the WENO'-NAH.[3]
Who will know? They are so teeny.
Yes, then let us call the atom
Something new like . . . HIAWATHA.[4]
That will be our really small joke.
That will be our MINNEHA'HA.[5]

1. The wild goose.

2. Wild rice.

3. Hiawatha's mother

4. Hero of Henry Wadsworth Longfellow's
   poem of 1855.

5. Laughing Water, wife of Hiawatha.

WHAT'S THE MATTER?

Miss Lucy had some matter.
She didn't know its state.
She only had three choices,
So tried to get it straight.

She thought it could be liquid,
Quite possibly a gas.
And if it wasn't solid,
Well call me sassafras.

Miss Lucy called the plumber.
Miss Lucy called the cop.
Miss Lucy called the egghead
With the perfectly bald top.

"Liquid," said the plumber.
"Solid," said the cop.
"Gas," said the egghead
With the perfectly bald, perfectly bald, perfectly bald
Top top top.

THE SENSELESS LAB
OF PROFESSOR REVERE

Listen, my children, and you shall hear,
Of how loud noises go in your ear.

And look, my youngsters, bright lights will be
The way you figure out how you see.

And feel, my students. Is that too much?
With gopher guts, you learn about touch.

And chew, my kiddies. Oh, what a waste.
That frog-eye stew was for you to taste.

And sniff, my scientists. Ain't it just swell
How ten-year-old cheese demonstrates smell?

So those are your senses. Class is done.
Next week—diseases! Won't that be fun?

AMOEBA

Don't ever tease a wee amoeba
By calling him a her amoeba.
And don't call her a he amoeba.
Or never he a she amoeba.
'Cause whether his or hers amoeba,
They too feel like you and meba.

CHANGES

I'm a little mealworm,
Short and wiggly.
Here's my antenna,
Cute and jiggly.

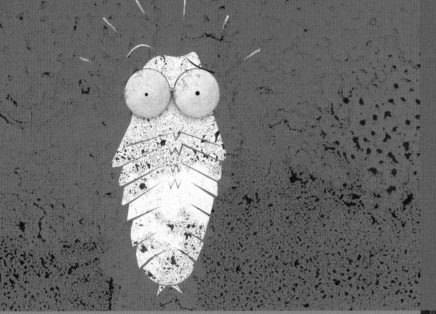

Now I am a pupa,
Squat and white.
How did this happen?
I'm a sight.

Now I am a beetle.
What is this?
I really hate
Metamorphosis.

'TWAS THE NIGHT

'Twas the night before Any Thing, and all through deep space,
Nothing existed—time, matter, or place.
No stockings, no chimneys. It was hotter than hot.
Everything was compressed in one very dense dot.

When out of the nothing there appeared with a clatter
A fat guy with reindeer and something the matter.
His nose was all runny. He gave a sick hack.
"Oh, Dasher! Oh, Dancer! I can't hold it back!"

He huffled and snuffled and sneezed one AH-CHOO!
Then like ten jillion volcanoes, the universe blew.
That dense dot exploded, spewing out stars,
Earth, Venus, Jupiter, Uranus, and Mars,

Helium, hydrogen, the mountains and seas,
The chicken, the egg, the birds and the bees,
Yesterday's newspaper, tomorrow's burnt toast,
Protons and neutrons, your grandma's pork roast.

The universe expanded. The guy said with a wheeze,
"Who will ever believe the world started by sneeze?
So let's call it something much grander, all right?
Merry BIG BANG to all! And to all—Gesundheit!"

ASTRONAUT STOPPING BY A PLANET ON A SNOWY EVENING

Which world this is I do not know.
It's in our solar system though.
I'm thinking that it might be Mars,
Because it has that reddish glow.

But you know it could be Venus.
And if that's true, then just between us,
It might be wise to leave before
Any locals might have seen us.

Could be Pluto. Might be Neptune.
Don't they both have more than one moon?
I'm running out of oxygen.
I'd better figure this out soon.

Yes space is lovely, dark and deep.
For one mistake I now do weep:
In science class I was asleep.
In science class I was asleep . . .

Asleep.
Asleep.
It's science class.
I am asleep.

WHACK! goes Mr. Newton's pointer on the blackboard.

"And that, my scientists, is the solar system. Test tomorrow on the planets.

Class dismissed."

Awake.

Awake. I am awake.

I'm thinking in regular sentences.

I'm not rhyming anymore.
I'm cured of my Science Verse.

THE UNIVERSE IS BEAUTIFUL.

And life is just great . . .
until art class, when Mr. Picasso says,

"**DO NOT** think of this as a little art project.
Your art project must be your **whole life.**"

OBSERVATIONS and Conclusions

1. Any similarity between "Evolution" and the chorus of "The Battle Hymn of the Republic" by Julia Ward Howe (1819–1910) . . . is very interesting.

2. Any resemblance between "Lovely" and the poem "Trees" by Joyce Kilmer (1886–1918) is pretty funny.

3. Any correspondence between "Twink—" and "The Star" by Ann and Jane Taylor (1782–1866 and 1783–1824) is really not that surprising.

4. Kind of spooky how "Dino-Sore" reminds you of "The Raven" by Edgar Allan Poe (1809–1849) isn't it?

5. How about that "Gobblegooky"? Seems to have a lot in common with "Jabberwocky" by Lewis Carroll (1832–1898). And I'm not talking about just the title.

6. Funny how much "Mary Had a . . ." sounds like "Mary's Lamb" by Sarah Josepha Hale (1788–1879).

7. Probably just a coincidence that "Scientific Method at the Bat" sounds exactly like "Casey at the Bat" by Ernest Lawrence Thayer (1863–1940).

8. Can you believe "Mini Ha Ha"? If you closed your eyes, you would think you were listening to "The Song of Hiawatha" by Henry Wadsworth Longfellow (1807–1882).

9. And speaking of Henry Wadsworth Longfellow (still 1807–1882), what do you make of "The Senseless Lab of Professor Revere"? A kissing cousin to "Paul Revere's Ride" by Mr. Longfellow is what I think.

10. Something about "'Twas the Night" is mighty like "A Visit from St. Nicholas" by Clement Clarke Moore (1779–1863). The guy in the red suit, for one thing.

11. "Astronaut Stopping by a Planet on a Snowy Evening" definitely reminds me of a poem by Robert Frost (1874–1963). Not "Mending Wall." Not "Fire and Ice." More like "Stopping by Woods on a Snowy Evening."

12. Any similarity between any of the other poems in *Science Verse* and any other poems in the rest of the known world is okay. Don't worry about it. The only poem that wasn't intentionally based on another poem is, for some reason, "Amoeba." No telling why.

1								
H								
Hydrogen								
1.0								

3	4
Li	**Be**
Lithium	Beryillum
6.9	9.0

11	12
Na	**Mg**
Sodium	Magnesium
23.0	24.3

19	20	21	22	23	24	25	26	27
K	**Ca**	**Sc**	**Ti**	**V**	**Cr**	**Mn**	**Fe**	**Co**
Potassium	Calcium	Scandium	Titanium	Vanadium	Chromium	Manganese	Iron	Coba
39.1	40.1	45.0	47.9	50.9	52.0	54.9	55.8	58.9

37	38	39	40	41	42	43	44	45
Rb	**Sr**	**Y**	**Zr**	**Nb**	**Mo**	**Tc**	**Ru**	**Rh**
Rubidium	Strontium	Yttrium	Zirconium	Niobium	Molybdenum	Technetium	Ruthenium	Rhodi
85.5	87.6	88.9	91.2	92.9	95.9	98	101.1	102.

55	56	57-71	72	73	74	75	76	77
Cs	**Ba**	**La**	**Hf**	**Ta**	**W**	**Re**	**Os**	**Ir**
Cesium	Barium	Lanthanides	Hafnium	Tantalum	Tungsten	Rhenium	Osmium	Iridiu
132.9	137.3		178.5	180.9	183.9	186.2	190.2	192.

87	88	89-103	104	105	106	107	108	109
Fr	**Ra**	**Ac**	**Rf**	**Db**	**Sg**	**Bh**	**Hs**	**Mt**
Francium	Radium	Actinides	Rutherfordium	Dubnium	Seaborgium	Bohrium	Hassium	Meitner
223.0	226.0		257	260	263	262	265	266